Raintree is an imprint of Capstone Global Library Limited, a company incorporated in England and Wales having its registered office at 7 Pilgrim Street, London, EC4V 6LB - Registered company number: 6695582

To contact Raintree please phone 0845 6044371, fax + 44 (0) 1865 312263, or email myorders@ raintreepublishers.co.uk. Customers from outside the UK please telephone +44 1865 312262.

Originally published by DC Comics in the U.S. in single magazine form as Superman Adventures #8.
Copyright © 2013 DC Comics. All Rights Reserved.

DC Comics
1700 Broadway, New York, NY 10019
A Warner Bros. Entertainment Company

First published by Stone Arch Books in 2013
First published in the United Kingdom in 2014
The moral rights of the proprietor have been asserted.

Ashley C. Andersen Zantop *Publisher*
Michael Dahl *Editorial Director*
Donald Lemke & Sean Tulien *Editors*
Heather Kindseth *Creative Director*
Bob Lentz *Designer*
Kathy McColley *Production Specialist*

DC COMICS
Mike McAvennie *Original US Editor*
Rick Burchett & Terry Austin *Cover Artists*

Originated by Capstone Global Library Ltd
Printed and bound in China by Leo Paper Products Ltd

ISBN 978 1 406 26680 1
17 16 15 14 13
10 9 8 7 6 5 4 3 2

British Library Cataloguing in Publication Data
A full catalogue record for this book is available from the British Library.

SUPERMAN ADVENTURES

A Big Problem!

Scott McCloud...................... writer
Rick Burchett ....penciller
Terry Austin .... inker
Marie Severin .... colourist
Lois Buhalis...................... letterer

Superman created by
Jerry Siegel & Joe Shuster

WHOOM!

WELL, YOU MAY WANT TO DO *SOMETHING* BEFORE HE GETS AROUND TO *THIS* BUILDING.

WE'VE GOT TO CHANGE JAX-UR BACK TO HIS *NORMAL* SIZE SOMEHOW.

HOPEFULLY, PROFESSOR HAMILTON STILL HAS THE SIZE-CHANGING DEVICE--

WHERE ARE YOU, KAL-EL? WE HAVE *UNFINISHED BUSINESS,* YOU AND I.

REMEMBER WHEN I SAID I WOULD *CRUSH YOU* LIKE A *BUG?*

--AND IS STILL *ALIVE!*

FLEA!! SMAK!

HOW DARE YOU?!

AARGGH!

OH, JEEZ, THEY GOT TURPIN, CHIEF!

HE'S HIT, AND HE'S FALLING FAST!

NO, WAIT! HE'S SLOWING DOWN!

LOOKS LIKE HE'LL LIVE, CHIEF...

THERE IS TO BE ONLY **ONE** SUCH AS I.

...

YES, GENERAL.

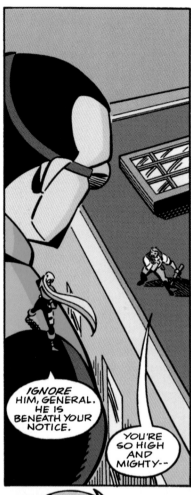

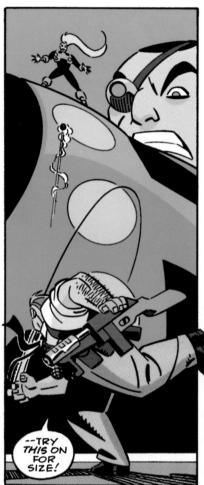

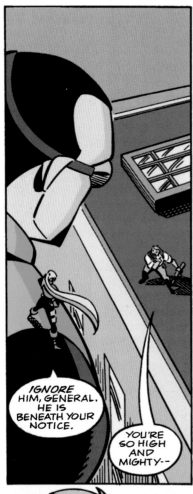

IGNORE HIM, GENERAL. HE IS BENEATH YOUR NOTICE.

YOU'RE SO HIGH AND MIGHTY--

--TRY THIS ON FOR SIZE!

WHOOMPH!

:Unnf!: YOU FOOL!

POW! POW! POW!

WHAT THE-- AARRGH!

PA-DOOOM!

"...BUT JUST *BARELY.*"

...SERIOUS, BUT STABLE CONDITION. WE'LL BE WATCHING HIM.

THAT STUBBORN MULE. HE NEVER KNOWS WHEN TO QUIT.

HE'S HAD MORE BROKEN LIMBS THAN THE *U.S. SKI TEAM!*

THAT WAS A FOOLISH STUNT YOU PULLED BACK THERE, DAN.

YOU HAVE A LOT OF GUTS, BUT NOT MUCH *BRAINS.*

SOMEBODY HAD TO DO *SOMETHING.* WHAT DO *YOU* PLAN TO DO, SMART GUY?

TO BE HONEST, DAN, I JUST DON'T KNOW. THE PRESIDENT HIMSELF ASKED ME TO KEEP MY DISTANCE UNTIL WE HAVE A WORKABLE PLAN.

HE SAYS THEY DON'T WANT TO WASTE ME ON A SUICIDE MISSION.

THIS ONE'S GOT YOU *SPOOKED,* DOESN'T IT?

I GUESS I JUST FEEL SO... *HELPLESS.*

HEY, IT DOESN'T MATTER WHAT *SIZE* YOU ARE, IF YOU'VE GOT THE GUTS, YOU CAN MAKE *ANYTHING* HAPPEN!

THAT GUY MAY LOOK *BIG* AND *TOUGH*, BUT *DEEP DOWN INSIDE* HE'S JUST AS--

WAIT!

THAT'S IT!

...REGGIE BANK'S REPORTING, WHERE THROUGHOUT THE NIGHT, THE EAST COAST HAS BEEN PARALYZED WITH *FEAR*, AS THE GIANT KRYPTONIAN JAX-UR AND HIS EVIL ACCOMPLICE, MALA, HEAD SOUTH FROM CITY TO CITY.

LATE-NIGHT EVACUATIONS WERE ORDERED FOR PHILADELPHIA AND BALTIMORE...

...AND CONTINUAL BOMBARDMENTS FROM TANKS AND NAVAL FIGHTERS HAVE BEEN UNSUCCESSFUL IN SLOWING THEIR ADVANCE TO THEIR PRESUMED DESTINATION--

I THINK HE'S ON TO ME! HE'S NOT OPENING HIS MOUTH!

TRY TICKLING HIM ON THE ROOF OF HIS MOUTH!

:Mmbph!:

DON'T LET HIM ESCAPE, GENERAL!

WHATEVER YOU DO, KEEP YOUR MOUTH CLOSED!

HOLD YOUR FIRE, MEN! HE'S COMING OUT!

DON'T GIVE IN, GENERAL!

GENERAL, DON'T! DON'T GIVE IN!

DON'T LET HIM ESCAPE!

YOU'VE GOT TO KEEP YOUR MOUTH CLOSED!

GLX! SHMZL! GLAH!

24

...AND THIS WAS THE SCENE LAST WEEK AS THE NOW-REMINIATURIZED KRYPTONIAN VILLAINS WERE CAUGHT ONCE AGAIN--

--AND PUT ONCE MORE SAFELY BEHIND BARS.

BOTH SUPERMAN AND S.T.A.R. LABS ASSURE THE PUBLIC THAT THE TERRORISTS' CELL HAS BEEN CREATED TO DAMPEN THEIR SUPER-POWERS FOR AS LONG AS THEY'RE IMPRISONED.

SUPERMAN, YOU'VE DESCRIBED THIS AS ONE OF THE MOST DIFFICULT BATTLES YOU'VE EVER FOUGHT.

THAT'S RIGHT...

...BUT WITH REAL-LIFE HEROES LIKE DAN TURPIN TO INSPIRE ME, I FEEL READY TO FACE UP TO ANY CHALLENGE.

INSPECTOR TURPIN, YOU HEARD WHAT THE MAN OF STEEL SAID ABOUT YOU. DO YOU CONSIDER YOURSELF A "HERO"?

AND WHAT IS THAT JOB, INSPECTOR?

NO WAY, BUDDY. I'M JUST DOIN' MY JOB LIKE ANYONE ELSE.

JUST KEEPIN' THE PEACE--

--AND LOOKIN' OUT FOR THE LITTLE GUY.

CREATORS

SCOTT McCLOUD WRITER

Scott McCloud is an acclaimed comics creator and author whose best-known work is the graphic novel *Understanding Comics*. His work also includes the science-fiction adventure series *Zot!*, a 12-issue run of *Superman Adventures*, and much more. Scott is the creator of the "24 Hour Comic", and frequently lectures on comics theory.

RICK BURCHETT PENCILLER

Rick Burchett has worked as a comics artist for more than 25 years. He has received the comics industry's Eisner Award three times, Spain's Haxtur Award, and he has been nominated for the Eagle Award in the UK. Rick lives with his wife and two sons in Missouri, USA.

TERRY AUSTIN INKER

Throughout his career, inker Terry Austin has received dozens of awards for his work on high-profile comics for DC Comics and Marvel, such as *The Uncanny X-Men*, *Doctor Strange*, *Justice League America*, *Green Lantern*, and *Superman Adventures*. He lives in New York, USA.

GLOSSARY

accomplice someone who helps another person commit a crime

complicated not simple; having lots of different parts or ideas which make it difficult to understand

confrontation open conflict between two or more sides

conquer defeat and take control of an enemy

din great deal of noise

dominion power to control something

faint dizzy and weak

intact complete, or not broken or harmed

presumed thought that something was true without being certain or having all the facts

psychopath someone who is mentally unbalanced, especially a person who is violent or dangerous

restore return something to an earlier or normal condition

stubborn not willing to accept change or help

SUPERMAN GLOSSARY

Intergang: an organized gang of criminals. They are armed with weapons supplied by the evil New Gods from the planet Apokolips. Their advanced weaponry makes them a threat to anyone, even the Man of Steel.

Jax Ur: an evil general from Krypton. Jax Ur is like Superman in that he receives superpowers from the yellow rays of Earth's sun.

Krypton: the planet where Superman was born. Brainiac destroyed Krypton shortly after Superman's parents sent him on his way to Earth.

Lois Lane: like Clark Kent, Lois is a reporter at the *Daily Planet* newspaper. She is also one of Clark's best friends.

Mala: a Kryptonian, like Superman and Jax Ur, Mala is given superpowers by the rays of Earth's yellow sun. She and Jax Ur were imprisoned in the Phantom Zone by Superman after they tried to destroy Metropolis.

Phantom Zone: an inter-dimensional prison for superpowered criminals. Those inside the Phantom Zone do not age, and cannot interact with anyone outside it.

Professor Hamilton: a brilliant inventor and scientist from S.T.A.R. Labs.

S.T.A.R. Labs: a research centre in Metropolis, where scientists make high-tech tools and devices for Superman and other heroes.

VISUAL QUESTIONS & PROMPTS

1 What is happening to Jax Ur in this panel? Could the artists have chosen to show the transformation in several panels instead? What would you have done if you were the artist? Why?

2 Why do you think the artists chose to zoom in close on Lois's eyeball in the second panel? Re-read the surrounding panels, then explain your answer.

GOT TURPIN, CHIEF!

HE'S HIT, AND HE'S FALLING FAST!

NO, WAIT! HE'S SLOWING DOWN!

1 Professor Hamilton's face is blurred in this panel. Why do you think the artists chose to show him this way?

SO! LING YOUR D SELF AGA···?

--OH!

OH, DEAR!

4 This sequence of four panels shows Superman flying towards Jax Ur from Superman's perspective. Why do you think the artists chose to show it from Superman's perspective and not Jax Ur's perspective?

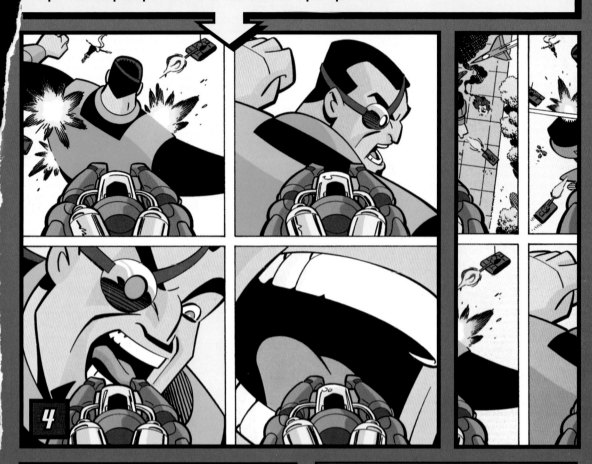

5 Why do you think the artists chose to show this illustration from a bird's-eye-view? Look at the surrounding panels on page 20 and explain your answer.

6 There are two meanings for the word "little" in Inspector Turpin's speech bubble. What do you think they are? Think about the plot of the story, then explain your answer.

JUST KEEPIN' THE PEACE--

--AND LOOKIN' OUT FOR THE LITTLE GUY.

SUPERMAN ADVENTURES